an
andrew greig's
that summer
with an enthusiast's view
by alan taylor

Scottish **Book** Trust

an extract from
andrew greig's
that summer

with an enthusiast's view
by alan taylor

2003

Published by
Scottish Book Trust
Scottish Book Centre
137 Dundee Street
Edinburgh EH11 1BG

Tel: 0131 229 3663

**From April 2003 Scottish Book Trust will be moving its offices
to Sandeman House, 55 High Street, Edinburgh EH1 1SR.**

ISBN: 1 901077 06 3
Copyright © Scottish Book Trust, 2003

Published with the support of the Scottish Arts Council National
Lottery Fund and The Hugh Fraser Foundation.

That Summer is published by Faber and Faber
ISBN: 0 571 20473 2

Extract copyright © Andrew Greig, 2000

Series design by Caleb Rutherford   eidetic
Printed in the UK by Cox & Wyman, Reading, Berkshire

contents

A note about *Read Around Books*   7

The enthusiast – Alan Taylor   9

The enthusiast's view   11

Extract from *That Summer*   19

About the author   39

Titles by Andrew Greig   41

Discussion points   42

Press quotes   43

Similar reads   44

Competition   46

Scottish Book Trust   47

Also available in the *Read Around Books* series   48

read **around books**

There is no shortage of fiction on the shelves of our bookshops – quite the opposite – but finding one that shouts out 'this is what you are looking for' is getting harder and harder as the number of books published goes up with each passing year. Too often we open a new book with expectation and enthusiasm only to discover disappointment and to struggle to get beyond page thirty. When we do find a book we really enjoy the urge is there to tell friends, colleagues and family to read it too in the hope that they will share our delight.

Read Around Books goes one step further and puts that enthusiasm down in black and white in the hope that many more readers will discover the joys of reading the very finest fiction that has emerged from Scotland over the last one hundred years. **This is a chance to sample before you borrow or buy**. Others have found these books before you, the writing held them spellbound and even when finished, these books would not let their readers go.

Each of the first twelve of these highly collectable little guide books promotes a work of fiction by a writer who lives in Scotland, was born in Scotland or who has been influenced by Scotland (our definition of Scottish is generous). Together they offer a marvellous introduction to the very best of Scottish writing from the twentieth and the first few years of the twenty-first centuries.

In each you will find a substantial extract, the enthusiast's view of the book, starting points for discussion for readers' groups, a short biographical piece about the author, and suggestions for similar reads which act as a further gateway to fine fiction.

Jan Rutherford
Series editor, 2003

the **enthusiast**

Alan Taylor

Alan Taylor is Associate Editor for the *Sunday Herald*. He is also a well-known literary critic and newspaper diarist and one half of the underperforming Scottish team on BBC Radio Four's 'Round Britain Quiz'. The year 2000 saw the publication of *The Assassin's Cloak: An Anthology of the World's Greatest Diarists* (Canongate) which he co-edited with his wife Irene and which was ten years in the making.

the enthusiast's view

That Summer
by Andrew Greig

The summer to which Andrew Greig's title refers is that of 1940. Britain was at war with Germany, led by Hitler and his monstrous regiment of Nazi stormtroopers. Though the Second World War was just months old, already much of Europe was in German hands. In September 1939, Poland was conquered; in April 1940, Denmark and Norway; during May and June 1940, the Netherlands and Belgium; and then the greatest, most portentous victory of all, France was defeated. Reeling from these defeats, Britain hastily withdrew from mainland Europe with the help of a makeshift armada. In July Hitler called on the British government to make peace. Even the British did not rate their chances of success. Germany, it appeared, held all the cards.

So grim was the situation that invasion was expected at any moment. On 20 July, 1940, Harold Nicolson, then Parliamentary Secretary to the Ministry of

Information, wrote in his diary: 'I think that Hitler will probably invade us within the next few days. He has 6,000 aeroplanes for the job. How strange it all is! We know that we are faced with a terrific invasion. We half-know that the odds are heavily against us. Yet there is a sort of exhilaration in the air. If Hitler were to postpone invasion and fiddle about in Africa and the Mediterranean, our morale might weaken. But we are really proud to be the people who will not give way.'

Though Nicolson rather over-estimated the number of planes which the Germans could call upon (they actually had 2,670 fighters and bombers), he accurately summed up the mood of a benighted nation. So, too, does Andrew Greig in *That Summer*, a splendid novel which creates with sparing detail and restrained emotion those harrowing days when countless lives hung by the flimsiest of threads. It is dedicated 'To the vanishing generation', a fitting testimonial to a generation of remarkable aviators who took to the skies in order to repel the advance of an abhorrent and rapacious regime. In what came to be known as the Battle of Britain, lay the salvation of a nation.

So far, so historical. But what Andrew Greig does best is create fiction, peopling it with convincing characters about whom you come to care deeply and passionately. Greig knows that one of the most outstanding features of war is its dullness. Soldiers like to say that war is ninety-nine percent boredom and one percent fright. The longer the boredom, the greater the fright. Greig uses boredom to heighten suspense. In the summer of

1940, the men who took to the air in defence of Britain spent long periods waiting for something to happen, killing time by playing darts, drinking beer, flirting with local women, reading, writing endless letters home, knowing that each one might be their last. They knew, too, that their moment would come. It is the waiting that gnaws away at them, increasing the paranoia.

That Summer opens with what could easily be a scene from a war movie, such as *The Dambuster*s, say, with planes and pilots returning or not from a mission. There is no nostalgia, no macho posturing, simply a brooding sense of expectation, of doom, of hindsight. Then we flash back to late June 1940, when Britain was almost a war innocent, its shores still free from attack. For many Britons war seemed so far off, so unthinkable, inconceivable. The same could not be said for the likes of Tadeusz, a Polish airman, whose country was so recently brutally and mercilessly subjugated. Tadeusz knows what to expect and it is the worst. For him, 'life is short but there are many possibilities'. So he smokes, drinks, and does not hang about where women are concerned, for tomorrow might be his last. In contrast, Len, a languid, working-class English man, who in my mind's eye owes something to George Orwell, can't quite comprehend what's happening. Life for Len may well be short but in the meantime he has a train to catch.

Greig casually, skilfully, subtly, captures the difference between those with and without war experience. His characters are representative of types which allow him to play around with ideas, such as nationalism, patriotism, heroism, class, gender. In counterbalance to Len and Tadeusz there are Stella and Maddy, two young women, the former classy, the latter fast, whose job it is to track enemy aircraft by radar. Unlike the men to whom they become inevitably attached, they work on the ground. But theirs is no safer an occupation since they are as prey to the Luftwaffe as the men who go up in Spitfires to intercept them. As the months of that languorous, hot, sensuous, oppressive summer – 'a summer seen through heat wave' – slip by and the reality of war takes hold, an age of innocence remorselessly gives way to knowledge that death is ever present.

That Summer is like reading wartime diaries, which flit between momentous events and domestic trivia. One minute people are concerned about getting a pint before last orders, the next they're contemplating Armageddon. Yet the war, that untouchable thing, never goes away, whatever one does. 'Wartime,' says Stella, 'is like real life but more so.' Kissing is better than thinking. Couples have sex outdoors because they haven't done so before and might never get the chance again. Words are unnecessary when feelings are so transparent, almost audible. 'This wasn't said but it hung over us like a cloud of midges,' reflects Len early in August, 'sorrow on account of the greed on account of the anxiety.'

Along the way, you learn a lot about that unforgettable summer, which had its own melancholy soundtrack: 'Red Sails in the Sunset', Duke Ellington's Mood Indigo, 'I'll Be Seeing You', Glenn Miller, 'I've Got You Under My Skin'. It's as if popular songs have taken the place of conversation. They're a form of emotional shorthand, which may be why they remain potent. They also transport us back more than sixty years to a time when people talked about going to 'the flicks' rather than the movies. Nothing locates quite like slang and Greig uses it liberally to evoke the era, a reminder that war is not only a time of technological revolution but also of linguistic invention. How many readers today know that 'tail-end Charlie' was an RAF phrase for the rear-gunner in an aircraft?

The pace of *That Summer* is especially telling. Greig controls mood through the length of his sentences, which seem elastic and slow when the skies are empty. But as soon as the propellers begin to rotate they speed up and shorten, dropping on to the page like bursts of gunfire: 'Rattle across my wings like someone running a rod along railings. The plane shakes, staggers. Damn! Stopped looking! Throw the stick to right corner, everything goes grey, just see a ME109 flash past me. Try to turn, get a wild shot in but he just dives and is gone. Don't feel sharp enough to turn on my back and go down after him. Turn after the bombers. They've split, one going down in flames. God, this happens so quick.'

In such circumstances, life seems cheap and survival random. There is little time to stand back and wonder why, to consider whether the war is just and worthy of the sacrifice. Len tries to talk about it to his father, who fought in the First World War, but he doesn't get very far. 'A lot of people died, son,' his father tells him. 'It's best not thinking about it. Best just get on with it.' The very fact that Len is willing to talk about it is an indication that society is changing, albeit slowly, the new, more irreverent generation less willing to toe the line.

There is also a sense of how war can break down barriers. In other novels about the Second World War, such as Evelyn Waugh's *Sword of Honour* trilogy, the class system is almost intact. But Greig shows, principally through the relationship of Len and Stella, that war can blur the divisions in society. In ways not obvious at the time, Britain was changing, not least because of events over the summer of 1940. We know what happened in the great scheme of things. We know that towards the end of August of that year, Churchill stood up in the House of Commons and gave thanks to the RAF for not buckling in the face of an enemy that was numerically far superior. 'Never in the history of human conflict has so much been owed by so many to so few,' he said. Hearing British planes flying overhead on their way to bomb Berlin on 26 August, Harold Nicolson wrote: 'I find one practises a sort of suspension of the imagination. I do not think that drone in the sky means death to many people at any moment. It seems so incredible as I sit here at my window, looking out on the fuchsias and zinneas with yellow butterflies playing around each other, that in a few seconds above the trees I may see other butterflies circling in the air intent on murdering each other. One lives in the present. The past is too sad a recollection and the future too sad a despair.' In *That Summer*, Andrew Greig takes us back to that awful present, lest we forget.

The extract

That Summer

To the vanishing generation

Firstword

*A*bove my bed, when I was young, the Airfix kits, the Hurricane, Spitfire, Messerschmitt, spun on their threads in the draught.

One by one they will return, throttling down over perimeter wires of forgotten airfields, then taxi up to abandoned huts. Down the bramble-choked lane come the women and men on bicycles, others on foot, the sound of their voices light and drifting as a summer swarm as they pass through the rusting gates, waving to the CO gliding by in his Lagonda.

The pilots jump down from their planes, knees bending as they hit the ground. A few stumble, awkward with their parachutes bumping at the back of their thighs. Some wave, some call, but their voices are so light they are borne away on the summer breeze. A faint rain is starting to fall and clings, shimmering, to their grey-blue uniforms.

The two groups meet and mingle. Handshakes and pats on the back. A hug and a light kiss on a cheek, postponed for sixty years. A black Labrador runs through legs and is greeted by a bulky man who kneels to embrace him. As they tussle, some drift over to the aircraft whose manifolds steam in the drizzle. These are mostly men, the fitters, riggers and armourers. They stroke the wings, run fingers over the blown-away fragments of cloth that once covered the gun ports, curse quietly.

Others look around in the rain at the rutted grass, the cracked concrete where the youth of the town race motorbikes and go-karts at weekends, the husks of Nissen huts. The control tower still stands though its windows are blank, the aerials bent and rusting. Some of the WAAFs move towards the concrete filter room, passing over the foundations of the communications hut. In the mud on the floor of the Anderson shelter one crouches and digs up the remains of an old *Picture Post*. She peels the pages apart and out falls a wizened French letter. She shrugs, others laugh. The youngest bites her lip.

Nearly all smoke. They pass cigarettes between them like benedictions, like tokens of belonging. After all, they need take no heed of health warnings, even if there were any on the packets they slip from breast pockets, flip open, light up, then breathe into the warm, damp air.

They talk in small groups. The pilots gesture with their hands, showing how it happened. They argue still over numbers and formations. One shows with the side of his hand dropping earthwards how he had peeled away, then steadied and came up behind his other hand, flying level. Then both start to shake. The others nod and laugh, quiet but persistent as memory.

So they talk and drift till the drizzle slows then stops. Cigarettes are squashed under shoes and flying boots, ties are pushed up under collars, caps are straightened or set at precise, jaunty angles that pass just inside regulations. The couple who have been entwined since the beginning come back from the woods by the perimeter fence. The bells of the bicycles ring faintly as they fade up the lane. The propellers blur as the engines rev in whispers. Then one by one they take off and climb above the clouds where it is always blue, burning and burning at that summer's end.

There are some radio telephone signals from that summer – pilots taking directions from the women who controlled them from the ground, or screaming at each other to get in formation – that have become trapped between the ground and the Heaviside layer. They bounce back and forward like tennis balls in some endless rally, for they don't decay. Once in a while a radio ham, idly skimming the airwaves late at night, will suddenly be listening to men and women controlling, flying, singing, cursing, dying. All present in the headphones though they are long gone.

And among the few trees that are left beyond the rusting perimeter fence, there is a trunk with large distorted letters bearing a name and a date. It was carved by the other one, the lanky tired one who stands half in, half out the bedroom window of a house in the post-war estate, his tan boots sunk a foot below the floor. The one with his long back turned, whose right arm hangs slightly crooked, who is always starting to turn round, who never fully turns round, whose face would be so familiar. Who speaks in the dark:

Chapter One

Late June 1940

First time I saw Tad he was standing in the Botanical Gardens near the station with a brown trilby shading his eyes and his foot on the stump of a 300-million-year-old fossilized tree. He was staring at it like a hunter gazing down at the lion he'd shot. The same look of awe and regret and ... something.

I lowered my heavy kitbag and stood near him, reading the plaque. Tried to imagine this part of England near the equator and covered in steamy swamps, the huge primitive trees towering over our heads. Thought of the great changes that had taken place, and of the one that was happening right now, and then it didn't seem quite so important and that was a relief.

The figure beside me stirred then straightened up. I felt his eyes flick over me, my uniform still blue and stiff, my kitbag.

'Yes, my friend,' he said, as though continuing a conversation. His voice was throaty and quite strongly accented. 'This is very old, you see.' He tapped the stone tree with a spotless brogue shoe. 'But we are alive and it is not. So we are one up.'

I nodded. So that had been the other part in his expression: quiet triumph. I nodded as though addressing strangers was normal, put it down to his foreignness. And the War.

'Yes,' I said. 'But what will be left of us?'

He laughed then. An easy laugh that I hadn't expected from his heavy, serious face.

'Nothing, my friend!' He held out his hand, it was surprisingly small. I automatically took it, as though this was quite normal. But then, very little was normal recently.

'So you are the gloomy type,' he said. 'I am Tadeusz. I am from Poland but not gloomy, you know.'

I didn't know if Tadeusz was his first or second name. He said it as though it was a title.

'Leonard Westbourne,' I said, 'though people call me Len.'

'Ah yes, the English nickname of intimacy! In that case, you may call me Tad, I think it simpler for you.'

His face suddenly lit up in a smile that brightened the grey day around us. But it wasn't directed at me. With a gesture at once formal and natural he removed his hat and inclined his head as he clicked his heels together. I looked round. A tall and strikingly pretty woman was approaching us.

'Good day, madam!' he said. 'I trust you are well?'

She hesitated. I watched several impulses chase across her face. *Who is this lunatic? Have we met before?* Then something in the warmth of his smile, the deference of his gesture must have reassured her.

'Very well, thank you,' she said. Then she walked on and past us but something about the set of her head suggested she was smiling.

Tad looked after her as if it pleased him to see something so fine. Then he clapped me on the shoulder.

'You see, Len,' he said, 'life is short but there are many possibilities. Was she not beautiful?'

'Maybe,' I said. I hefted my kitbag onto my shoulder. 'But I've a train to catch.'

Then without the trilby shading them, I saw his eyes. They were near-black, hot and restless and suddenly serious.

'Yes,' he said. 'We do not forget the War. Never!'

He said it with such conviction as if it were a curse, such passion that could never be English. Then he put his hand on my arm.

'Come, my friend, let us go to the station and join our squadron and fight this war.'

I stared at him, at his expensive suit. He was quite short and wide, big-boned. With his hunched shoulders and large mobile head and hot dark eyes he suddenly reminded me of a hawk. That same concentrated force. He looked back at me and chuckled at my astonishment.

'You are Sergeant Westbourne, are you not? I am told you are joining with me and you will be catching this afternoon train. Why do you think I introduce myself? My luggage awaits at the station, you know.'

He put his trilby on and adjusted the brim down over his eyes.

'If we hurry, there may be time for a drink of your

warm beer at the station bar. There were two women there, very pretty...'

I hesitated outside the pub. In front of me was the public bar, which looked seedy, especially for someone as immaculately overdressed as my new companion. I suggested we went in the lounge. More comfortable.

He shook his head, sorrowfully it seemed.

'Leonard, I am not bourgeois!' he announced grandly. 'Lounge bar is for the stuffy and the bourgeois. But Tadeusz Polarczyk is intelligentsia and you are a peasant, yes?'

He pronounced my peasant status in such a matter-of-fact way it was impossible to be offended.

'Yes,' I said. 'I suppose I am a peasant.'

'So we drink in the public bar among the people!'

'Fine,' I said. 'You're buying and please don't call anyone else in there a peasant. They mightn't like it.'

Inside we quickly drank to our good health, then caught the train at a run. So many possibilities, he'd said, and I felt them all around me that evening as the train ground south towards the coast, as solid yet ghostly as that once-living tree turned to stone.

* * *

So I just caught the bus at a run as it left the end of Green Road. The conductress stood watching inside and she wasn't smiling.

'It's forbidden to join a moving bus, Miss,' she announced.

I paused halfway up the stair to get my breath back.

'You might have waited for me,' I said.

This time she positively scowled. She wore brown heavy-rimmed glasses and they were just made for scowling.

'If we waited for everyone who's late, we'd never leave the station. Then where would we be?'

'In the station, stupid,' I muttered as I turned and went on up the stair. I half expected her to add *There's a war on, you know*, which seemed to have already become a catch phrase justifying any shortage or stupidity. People had said it as a joke during the phoney war, but now with the fall of France it wasn't so funny.

Upstairs was packed and smoky. There was one place left next to a woman with a pile of yellow hair.

'Excuse me, please,' I said.

She picked her bag off the seat, put it on her knee then glanced at me. She was younger than I'd thought, my age. I felt her take in my uniform, the new duffel bag containing my papers from the training school.

'Thank you,' I said, and sat down.

She took the cigarette from her full mouth, tapped the ash on the floor.

'You're welcome, love.'

Then she buried her head in the magazine she was reading. One of the cheaper, gossipy sort. The conductress came up and I paid my fare. She didn't go away but stared at the magazine my companion was half hidden behind.

'Fare, please,' she snapped. 'I'm talking to you, Missie.'

There was a long pause then the magazine came down. Big blue eyes set around with make-up.

'I've forgotten my purse,' she said. 'Sorry. I'll get off at the next stop.'

'Sorry! There's honest people on this bus pay their fare, but not you. Don't you know there's–?'

'It's all right,' I said. 'She's with me. I'm paying.'

'Thanks,' she said. 'Thanks so much. Did you see that old bat's face?'

'Yes,' I said. 'That was well worth a few pennies.'

'Like a smoke?'

She held out the packet. Du Maurier. I'd tried as a child, then again at university, but never really got into the habit.

'Thanks,' I said.

We lit up together and I tried not to cough. I blew smoke out into the thick blue-grey fug. Hard to remember what it was like, upstairs in buses in those days.

'I'll pay you back,' she said. 'You're on this bus regular. I seen you before.'

'No need,' I said. 'Really.'

'Thanks. I thought you were toffee-nosed but you're a good sort. Still, doing the bus company is one thing, doing a pal is another.'

I sat with the warm glow of that 'pal'. Truth is, I was lonely in my billet in the town, getting my training through the week, going home at weekends. My university friends had gone their ways, and as for boyfriends, well, I didn't want to think about that.

I finished the cigarette and got up.

'My stop,' I said.

'Tell you what,' she said. 'Let's go to that Lyons across the street and I'll get you coffee and a cake.'

'But I thought—'

She smiled then, big and wide. Lots of white teeth. I'd see that smile, hear that laugh many times before we were through with that summer.

'I was at school with a waitress there,' she said. 'We used to skip off lots together. If I ask, she might just lose our bill. So?'

I contemplated this world in which people tried to avoid paying on buses, lost bills and didn't go to school, and didn't even feel guilty about it. My mother would be shocked. Alarmed that I would even associate with such a person, as though such a condition might be contagious. As though I might sink back into the class she'd striven to climb out of, the steamy swamp of the Unrespectable.

'Thanks,' I said. 'That sounds great.'

And as we stepped down from the bus, she said, 'I'm Maddy, by the way.'

'Stella,' I said. 'Stella Gardam.'

Then we went for coffee and cake in Lyons and the bill never appeared. I have to say the cake tasted all the sweeter for it, and the coffee had an edge I rather liked. And she told me she was a Naval VAD and how she had her hands full with an outbreak of mumps but the sailors were a load of laughs. I told her I was training in signals but it was hush-hush and I mustn't say more about it. Work with Radio Direction Finding – what would become Radar – was still a big secret. We'd yet to find just how important it was, back at the end of June that summer, before the battle had really started.

We stood outside on the pavement. I was about to say goodbye and walk back to my digs.

'Here,' she said. 'Fancy going to a RAF dance on Friday? I know the drummer in the band, we can get in free.'

I thought about it. A weekend at home with my mother and respectability. Dad out with the ARP. And I had revision to do.

'That sounds fun,' I said. 'I'd love to.'

And so Maddy Phillips and I met, and so we went to the dance, and so ... everything.

Chapter Two
Early July

Yet how light a girl is when you dance, how far removed from a machine! She was pushed my way at the dance once Tad had bowed, clicked heels, seized her friend and whisked her off onto the dance floor. This one looked startled, then amused as we introduced ourselves. I missed the moment to shake hands and just nodded and grinned at her like an idiot, though an enthusiastic one.

'I expect you want to dance,' she said neutrally. Beyond her name, her first words to me.

'Well, yes,' I said. 'Do you?'

She glanced across the dance floor where Tad and her pal were spinning through the crowd. Then she looked me carefully down and up. When she smiled, two faint vertical lines appeared between her eyebrows.

'Yes,' she said.

We looked at each other a moment. I was sweating but wasn't going to let her have it all her own way.

'So,' she said at last, 'are you asking me?'

'I expect so,' I said, then she laughed and I took her right hand and for the first time placed my hand on her firm waist as we caught the beat and swung into a quickstep.

Stella Gardam looked good to me – glowing, chin up, pretty and funny and clever, you could tell. And probably way out of my class. Finished university, no less, now training at something she couldn't tell me about.

'Hush-hush,' she'd whispered in my ear as we turned a foxtrot at the corner of the crowded hall, Tad and her friend having disappeared.

'Oh, go on,' I said. 'Do I look like a spy?'

She leaned back in my arms and looked up at me.

'You look like an honest man,' she said eventually. 'But it's hard to tell these days.'

'Go on,' I said. 'Please.'

The clarinet squawked, the violin went *Aaw* and made it sound almost like harmony.

'All right,' she said, then stretched up to my ear.

'Radio Direction Finding,' she whispered. 'I'm learning to see what's coming our way.'

For a moment I looked into her eyes – wide-set, grey, looking straight back at me, calm and measuring.

'I don't know if that's such a good idea,' I said, and it came out more serious than I'd meant, and made her look away for a moment.

Tad and Stella's friend, a cheery bouncing blonde called Maddy, reappeared as the band was packing up. They seemed wrapped in some secret glow or joke. Tad proposed we all met up again soon as possible. I made with the eager nods while he kissed hands and bowed all over the shop and generally cut a dash. To my amazement the women were persuaded, we found a date we could all make, and a place – they were billeted just a couple of miles away. So: the Darnley Arms, twenty hundred hours, God and Goering willing.

Outside in the warm dark, she kissed me on the cheek. Then, as I hesitated, kissed me again, however briefly, on the mouth. Her lips were warm, dry, light. She went back down onto her heels and looked at me.

'Sometimes forewarned is forearmed,' she said. 'I didn't know I was going to do that. Did you?'

A sparky girl. Something in her look is a challenge I would rise to.

'It was a dead cert,' I said. 'Didn't need no RDF to tell me.'

I got a quick grin, then she squeezed my arm and walked away. Two shadows detached themselves from behind the hall and Maddy came into the light again and caught up with Stella, straightening her dress. Well, Tad had made his intentions clear enough (*I want rolling that Maddy from here to Cracow*) and she seemed to have no objections at all.

We walked home through the warm darkness, humming 'Red Sails in the Sunset'.

'Did you and Maddy–?' I asked. No answer but his laugh.

* * *

He's not what I'd pictured. Not even an officer, for a start. No moustache (not many of them do, that's for the older ones, the desk men left from the last war). And he's not posh – quite a marked West Country accent, his father works a lathe in some factory, and while my mother would doubtless describe his background as 'salt of the earth', I doubt if she'd want it sprinkled on her back garden, or on her daughter. (Not that it will come to that.)

He's a bit gangly and gauche is Mr Len Westbourne. Maybe this is what I liked about him, that he was embarrassed and stood there like he didn't know what to do when Maddy pushed me towards him at the dance. Because I didn't know what to do either – I mean, I'd only gone to keep Maddy company, not looking for a man.

So I teased him to relieve my own embarrassment. As I waited for a response I wondered if he was slow, and I can't stand slow. But he stood up for himself and forced me to ask if he was asking, because I suddenly did want to dance. No harm in having some fun, just because there's a war on.

To my surprise he danced not badly and was good in the turns. He led well, not bossy, just letting the rhythm push us both around. He knows it's *funny*, dancing, and for that I liked him. I hadn't had a man hold me like that since Evelyn, and before that, of course, Roger of cursed memory.

Anyway, though we'd accepted the date, we'd no real intention of going to meet them at the Darnley. At least, I hadn't. Far as I was concerned, if Maddy wanted a roll under the hedge with our admittedly well-groomed Polish friend, there was no need to drag me along. But though I'd only nodded, I felt somehow implicated, and his face had lit up so . . .

No, I had other things to concentrate on. I'd keep my head well below the parapet on the romantic front for a while yet.

* * *

Then we heard the guns around Gravesend as they hit the docks again, broke off the darts match to step outside and watch the show. It wasn't much at that distance, looked more like a nuisance raid than anything big. Since the fall of France we were still waiting for the real thing; it had to come sooner or later. In the meantime, we were free to fanny about.

'So why ain't you lads up there, knockin' 'em down?' one of the locals asked.

I said nothing, just watched our searchlights drain to nothing in the dark. It was rumoured the ack-ack was a waste of time, couldn't shoot high enough. But the gunners had to keep their spirits up, and reassure the public something was being done. I felt for those blokes, running around with their helmets slipping over their eyes, banging off rounds at invisible aircraft while knowing their shells fell short. So pointless, so human.

'His momma is not letting Lennie fly at night,' Tad growled. 'It stunts his growing, you know. And me, I have never liked the overtime.'

In the dark street I smiled to myself, though our return fire was just a gesture. I'd noticed Tad's English was good except when it suited him, like when dealing with an irate CO or teasing the natives.

'Let's hope you shoot better than you speak English, mate,' one of them said.

These lads were set on beating us, and with their home crowd looking on it was friendly, but a bit of needle too, no doubt. We shrugged, turned away and went back into the pub, nothing we could do. Tad was right, we were no nightfighters.

And I'm no darts player, never have been. Too much time to get tense, to start to doubt myself. As a lad with my dad's old .22, I was always better at a moving target. So exciting to have that power at a distance, hear the crack, feel the recoil and see the rabbit fall over just like that. And I loved rabbit stew. It was the bit in the middle I didn't like, the glazed eye, the blood.

In any case, draughtsmanship has always been my thing, not chatting up women. Though I'd thought this time I'd got lucky. But there was still no sign of Stella and Maddy (a wild one, suitable mate for Tad, I reckoned). I glanced at my watch as Tad picked up the darts. An hour late. Not much chance they'd be coming now. I thought again of those ack-ack gunners, shooting off shells knowing it was useless.

Our opposition, Dave and Tom, two local lads we'd met that evening while jostling for bar space in the Darnley, were frankly in a different class. But we'd had a couple while waiting for the women, and we'd hit one of those hot streaks that comes once in a while, and we were holding them. With their mates watching and making with the wisecracks, it had turned into a bit of a do. Not what I had in mind for the evening, but it was all that was on offer.

So I took a quick drag and went up to the mark to throw. Went for 19, hit treble 17, pinged one off the wire then on impulse switched to 20 and picked up a double. It had been like that all evening. Lucky in darts if not in love.

We won that game. Three-all. A last decider. I got another round in first. No hurry, after all we had nothing better to do.

Shame, really. For a moment I'd thought it might happen.

But our date had always been a speculative shot. We weren't officers, I'm no Clark Gable, and Tad's just too different for most. I checked my watch again. Nearly an hour and a half late. Finish the game, one more drink then leave.

They got away first throw but so did we, and chased each other down great style from 501. Suddenly I was standing with 50 to shoot, three arrows in my hand, the local aces needing only double tops to wrap it up.

'When the going gets tough . . .' Tad whispered. 'You can do it, Lenny.'

I put down my cigarette, casual like, and toed the line. With the room silent and all eyes on me, I hit the 10. Then went for tops. Tensed on it, hit the ruddy wall. Someone laughed, I hesitated, and in that bright room felt alone, not tough at all. Certain of defeat, I drew my arm back anyway.

The street door opened. I saw Stella's eyes on me, wide forehead beneath that permed-up sweep of auburn hair, and Maddy right behind her. I glanced, turned back to the board, threw.

The moment it left my hand I was sure. Nothing, no bombs, no ruddy war could change it now. My dart slid through the smoky air and thudded into double 20.

Hubbub, laughter, Tad's whoop. Mine host set us up a pint apiece while we shook hands with Dave and Tom.

'Won't be so lucky next time,' Dave muttered, and I rather agreed as we pushed over to our girls. She smiled, I smiled. For that moment there seemed no flap, no worry. Though she had class, I had my moments and that might do. Would blooming have to!

'What was all the fuss about?' she asked.

'We got lucky and won against the run of play,' I replied.

'I see,' she said. 'Maybe it's as well we were late. Missed the boring bit.'

But she took my arm, just like that, as we went through to the Snug. And when we were seated with the beers and gins and she turned to me again, I seemed to see what she'd say next, what I'd say, how it would all turn out, as though a searchlight had just leapt forward in the dark and we had always been its mark.

about the **author**

Andrew Greig

A ndrew Greig was born in Bannockburn in 1951, and was brought up there and on the Fife coast. It was the upbringing of a generation he feels to be deeply cast in the shadow of war. Whereas those who had fought and lived through the war were struggling for normality and happy families, the war left a more glamorous legacy for those not born into it. As a child, Andrew was fixated by the idea of flying. His boyhood ambition of becoming a pilot was to be dashed by less than 20/20 vision – making Airfix models and later flying them became the reality of the dream.

Andrew completed his MA in Philosophy at Edinburgh University. He has received an Eric Gregory Award and a Scottish Arts Council bursary; he was writer-in-residence at Glasgow University from 1979 to 1981 and Scottish/Canadian Exchange Fellow 1982–3. He now lives in Orkney with his wife, novelist Lesley Glaister.

Andrew's first novel, *Electric Brae*, was shortlisted for

the McVitie's Prize and the Boardman-Tasker Award and his second, *The Return of John MacNab*, topped the Scottish bestseller lists in 1996. His novel *When They Lay Bare* was published by Faber in 1999.

He is recognised as one of the leading Scottish poets of his generation, having written six volumes of poetry. He is also well known for his writing on mountaineering, and has written two books describing his climbing experiences in Scotland and the Himalayas – *Summit Fever* and *Kingdoms of Experience*. Both books were shortlisted for the Boardman-Tasker Award for mountaineering literature.

Much of the inspiration for *That Summer* is drawn from his childhood and from the experiences of his parents during the Second World War: Andrew's parents met during the Second World War; both had been engaged to people who were killed in action; his father was in charge of an evacuated maternity hospital and his mother was a Naval VAD nurse. It was only when Andrew Greig started to write *That Summer* that his mother started talking to him about that period in her life. Indeed, she gave him the journal she kept from 1939–40, parts of which have now been incorporated into the novel.

titles **by**

Andrew Greig

Poetry
Men on Ice
Surviving Passages
A Flame in Your Heart
The Order of the Day
Western Swing

Mountaineering
Summit Fever
Kingdoms of Experience

Fiction
Electric Brae
The Return of John MacNab
When They Lay Bare

discussion **points**

1. *That Summer* is a historical novel. How important is it to get historical details correct in fiction?

2. How do you think *That Summer* would have been received had it been published during the war?

3. What can fiction teach us that history can't?

4. What does *That Summer* tell us about the role of women in the war?

5. Andrew Greig is also a well-known poet. How poetic is his prose?

6. Would you agree that while commemorating the bravery of the Battle of Britain pilots, Greig is careful not to celebrate them?

press quotes

'The Battle of Britain may be rightly regarded as the most famous air conflict in history but Greig has made it something much more important for a generation now almost unimaginably removed: he has made it real ... *That Summer* is an extraordinary achievement that deserves to have Greig, after several impressive novels, promoted to the ranks of the highest-regarded writers.'
– Anthea Lawson, *The Times*

'A novel of great power, intelligence and delicacy... a remarkable achievement, by far the best thing Andrew Greig has done, and a book which establishes him as a very considerable novelist.'
– Allan Massie, *Scotsman*

'Greig's achievement is to let us smell the flowers through the smoke, pain and confusion. This is a lovely book.' – Peter Cunningham, *Irish Times*

similar **reads**

Flight to Arras by Antoine de Saint-Exupéry
(Penguin Books; ISBN: 0141183187)
Translated from the French, where the title was Pilote
de Guerre. *First published in 1942.*
A short but powerful autobiographical novel in
which Saint-Exupéry tells of his and his crew's
experience on a futile mission in 1940 over the
burning city of Arras.

The Soldier's Art by Anthony Powell
(Mandarin; ISBN: 0749306505)
First published in 1966.
The eighth volume in Powell's *Dance to the Music of
Time* series takes place during the occupation of Paris
by the Germans in 1940 and their disastrous invasion
of Russia in the same month a year later.

Love is Blue by Joan Wyndham
(Flamingo; ISBN: 0006542018)
First published in 1986.
An hilarious (and apparently true) account of life in
the Women's Auxiliary Airforce in the early years of
the war.

The Naked and the Dead by Norman Mailer
(Flamingo; ISBN: 0586091157)
First published in 1949.
A classic war novel, set in the Second World War in the Far East, which shows unflinchingly the brutality of modern warfare.

Reach for the Sky by Paul Brickhill
(Cassell Military; ISBN: 0304356743)
First published in 1954.
The astonishing story of Douglas Bader who, despite losing both his legs in a plane crash before the war, insisted on flying against the Germans and emerged a hero.

Catch-22 by Joseph Heller
(Vintage; ISBN: 0099477319)
First published in 1961.
The absurdity and chaos of war memorably and comically depicted through a group of unforgettable characters.

competition

**Your chance to win ten contemporary works
of fiction signed by their authors.**

The *Read Around Books* series was developed by Scottish
Book Trust to encourage readers to widen their reading
interests and discover writers they had never tried before.
Has it been a success? We want to hear from you. Tell us
if you have enjoyed this little series or not and if you did,
do you have any suggestions for authors who should be
included in the series in the future.

Writer to us now with the following information:

> Name and address
> Email address
> Are you a member of a readers' group?
> Name of readers' group

**Send us the information above and we will enter you
into our prize draw to be drawn on 22 August 2003.**

> Send to:
> RAB Draw
> Scottish Book Trust
> 137 Dundee Street
> Edinburgh EH11 1BG

scottish **book trust**

What is Scottish Book Trust?

Scottish Book Trust exists to serve readers and writers in Scotland. We work to ensure that everyone has access to good books, and to related resources and opportunities.

We do this in a number of ways:

- By operating the Writers in Scotland Scheme, which funds over 1,400 visits a year by Scottish writers to a variety of institutions and groups
- By supporting Scottish writing through a programme of professional training opportunities for writers
- By publishing a wide variety of resources and leaflets to support readership
- By promoting initiatives such as National Poetry Day and World Book Day
- And through our Book Information Service, providing free advice and support to readers and writers, and the general public.

For more information please visit
www.scottishbooktrust.com

titles **in the series**

Available in the Read Around Books series

Iain Crichton Smith's *Murdo: The Life and Works,*
  by Douglas Gifford

Meaghan Delahunt's *In The Blue House,*
  by Gavin Wallace

Michel Faber's *Under the Skin,* by Mary Firth

Jonathan Falla's *Blue Poppies,* by Rosemary Goring

Janice Galloway's *Clara,* by David Robinson

Andrew Greig's *That Summer,* by Alan Taylor

Anne MacLeod's *The Dark Ship,* by Lindsey Fraser

Maggie O'Farrell's *After You'd Gone,* by Rosemary Goring

Suhayl Saadi's *The Burning Mirror,*
  by Catherine McInerney

Ali Smith's *Hotel World,* by Kathryn Ross

Muriel Spark's *The Comforters,* by Alan Taylor

Alexander Trocchi's *Young Adam,* by Gillian Mackay